Tessa and Jamila put a heavy red box on
the table.
'Good,' said Mr Belter.

Mr Belter opened the top.
He asked the children to look inside.
'It is only a pile of grass and some old leaves,'
said Rocky.

'But look,' said Mr Belter.
He was moving the grass and leaves away.
Tessa jumped. 'It is a snake!' she shouted.

3

There was a rat-a-tat-tat at the door.
'Mr Keeping is going to talk about his snake,'
said Mr Belter.

Mr Keeping took the snake out of the box.

The children could see it moving all over
Mr Keeping.
'Bruce is a lovely snake,' said Mr Keeping.
'He will not hurt you.'

Mr Keeping put Bruce on Jamila.
'I have met Bruce,' said Jamila. 'I like him,
but he is heavy!'

All the children wanted to see the snake.
All the children but Tessa.
She did not like it.

Kevin had the snake.
He pushed it at Tessa.
'No!' shouted Tessa. 'Get it off me!'
'Stop that!' said Mr Belter.

Kevin did stop.
He was about to give the snake to
Mr Keeping.
He looked at his hands.

There was strange stuff on his hands.
'What is it?' shouted Kevin.

'The snake has shed its coat, and it came off
on your hands,' said Mr Keeping.
'Snakes do that!'

'Quick! Get it off me!' shouted Kevin.
He could have dropped the snake, but
Mr Keeping grabbed it.

Mr Keeping took the snake.

Kevin ran out of the room to get the
snake coat off his hands with hot water.

Tessa smiled.
'I do like snakes after all!' she said.